The Birds Are Yours

ROBERT S. LEMMON

WITH ILLUSTRATIONS BY

DON ECKELBERRY

The Macmillan Company

NEW YORK : 1951

Contents

765881

Birds Illustrated

THE BIRDS ARE YOURS

Orioles often return to the old home, as leg banding proves

Back to the Old Home

THE URGE TO RETURN
YEAR AFTER YEAR IS A
PROVED FACT

IN THE AVERAGE CASE it is impossible to be certain that the oriole nesting this year in your elm tree or the phoebe hatching a brood under your garage eaves is the same one that was there last season, but there's a fair chance that it is. Identifications by means of freak coloring or song peculiarities indicate that many individuals migrate northward in the spring to their old localities. Some even come back to the same yard and occasionally fix up the old nest and use it again.

The increasing practice of tracing bird movements by means of identification leg bands furnishes still stronger proof of this tendency to return to the old home. Among many such banding records are those of a purple finch that returned for four successive years, several golden-crowned sparrows that reappeared for three years, and a Baltimore oriole that did the same. As time goes on we can look for increasing evidence that numerous birds, like people, like to revisit the old home grounds.

Duck plumage is amazingly dense, waterproof and warm

[4]

Water Off a Duck's Back

ANY DUCK CAN SHOW YOU
EXACTLY HOW IT'S DONE

THERE ARE SEVERAL angles to a duck's ability to keep its skin dry and its body warm even when swimming under water. Taken together, they constitute as fine protection against catching cold as any bird could ask.

These safeguards begin with a thick skin normally underlaid by a substantial layer of fat and surfaced with a coat of short, very fluffy down. Then come the true body feathers, great numbers of them so compactly formed and overlapped that they constitute a blanket virtually impervious to either moisture or cold. Practically all water birds are similarly equipped.

Here, then, are the physical protective properties of body fat and a dense overcoating of feather growth. The latter is supplemented by large surface-opening oil glands at the base of the tail whose secretion is picked up by the bird's bill when preening and distributed throughout the true feathers to increase their natural oiliness. Small wonder that, whether he's swimming or just standing in the rain, the water literally runs right off a duck's back.

[5]

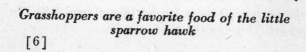

Grasshoppers are a favorite food of the little sparrow hawk

[6]

What Hawks Really Eat

THEIR DIET IS FAR MORE
VARIED THAN MANY
PEOPLE SUSPECT

MORE THAN FIFTY years ago the U. S. Department of Agriculture conducted scientific studies of the stomach contents of nearly 1800 North American hawks representing thirteen species, with a view to determining the extent to which we are justified in considering them as serious killers of poultry and other birds. The results were revealing, to put it mildly.

In only four kinds did the percentage of stomachs containing remains of poultry and various wild birds exceed those showing no trace of such foods. Of these four, the duck hawk led with 80 per cent, followed by the pigeon hawk with 76, Cooper's with 64, and sharp-shinned with 63. With all other kinds, including the big "hen hawks" which farmers used to consider their bitter enemies, the predominating food consisted of creatures that we ordinarily deem pests, such as small mammals like rats and mice, grasshoppers and other insects, snakes, frogs and so on. The short-tailed, Swainson's and rough-legged hawks had a hundred-per-cent clean record—no bird remains whatever.

[7]

Cardinals and many other birds may like to mate for life

Some Mate for Life

AN INCLINATION toward lifetime bird marriages is a hard matter to determine accurately, partly because the individuals of any given species are so identical in appearance that you can't tell one from another. Also, the annual death rate among wild birds is extremely high, with the result that few matings have the chance to run their full course and thereby prove a case one way or the other.

Such records as we have, however, indicate that the tendency to mate for life may be more widespread than most people think. It is believed that cardinals have it, as well as eagles, ravens, pigeons and doves, some of the hawks, Canada geese, and the comical little nuthatch. Probably these are only a small percentage of the actual total.

It by no means follows, however, that there is much if any truth in those stories about birds being so saddened by their mates' deaths that they never remarry. If that were the case, billions of wild birds would be grieving widows or widowers.

*A shrike has hung a golden-crowned kinglet
on a thorn tree*

When Death Is a Virtue

WITHOUT IT CHAOS
WOULD COME TO THE
WHOLE BIRD WORLD

NATURE IS the complete realist, notwithstanding her reputation as a kindly and tolerant old soul. Faced with the inconceivably complex duty of governing millions of different forms of life, many of them hostile to each other, she has to kill almost as much as she creates. In her balance book death rates as a high virtue.

If this sounds like a strange statement, consider the situation if all the descendants of a single pair of robins were to live out the full life span of five years or so allotted to their species. Ordinarily an average pair of robins raises two broods of four each per season, and projecting these figures ten years into the future with allowance for the matings of younger generations would give the original pair nearly 4,000,000 descendants. Such arithmetical progression applies to other species, too, and first thing you knew there would be far more birds in the world than there was food to support them. So, as a safeguard for all, we find a staggering percentage of accidental and violent deaths.

The long-lived bald eagle uses the same nest for years

How Long Do Birds Live?

IT ALL DEPENDS ON LUCK
AND WHO THEY ARE

PREDICTING the length of a bird's life is a good deal like trying to answer that old trick question, "How long is a piece of chalk?" With so many perils lurking just around the corner, any wild bird survives largely by luck and watchfulness. The percentage of deaths before middle age is far higher than among human beings, due in great part to the hazards to which all birds are constantly exposed. The best anyone can do is to lay down some rather general principles which, on the basis of known facts, throw interesting light on the situation.

First, species that lay only a few eggs each year are likely to live longer than the large-clutch kinds—naturally enough, since one of Nature's big aims is to maintain a normal total population for each of her innumerable forms of life. Also, within any broad group (sparrows, woodpeckers or warblers, let's say) there is a tendency for the larger kinds to live longer than the smaller ones, because of superior strength and all-around ruggedness.

Similarly, really big, strong fellows, like eagles, ducks

and geese, and the larger hawks and owls, usually live a good deal longer than smaller and weaker birds; forty or fifty years are a possibility for some of them, if they are unusually lucky.

The ordinary fully grown wild thrush, blue jay, or brown thrasher, on the other hand, probably lives only three or four years. And it is doubtful if such really small and fragile kinds as warblers and many of the sparrows can stick it out for even that time.

All these calculations are based, to a considerable extent, on individual observations over many years and, more accurately, on a slowly increasing mass of evidence provided by the bird-banding records noted elsewhere in this book. In part, too, they have been deduced from known facts on the life duration of birds that have been kept under ideal captivity conditions, as in the large flying cages of some zoological and private parks. This latter source of knowledge has also led to the conclusion that nearly all kinds of birds are physically capable of living twice as long as they actually do in the wild state, which gives you an idea of the tremendous numbers that are cut down before their time by starvation and various forms of accidental and violent death when Nature has her free way.

Yes, it does seem like an inexcusably wasteful system, by our standards. But in the over-all view it is the exact opposite of that. The death of every bird contributes its mite to the continuing existence of some other form of life, except as man may throw the machine out of balance by interfering with its operations as they were decreed long, long ago. That has often been done, particularly by the white race, and too often it has led to vast wildlife disasters.

Some Birds Are Nest Robbers

SOME NOT ONLY STEAL THEIR BOOTY, BUT ALSO EAT IT

OF THE seven hundred different species that make up our North American bird population, the great majority live in peace and harmony with each other, avoiding all but occasional mild friction. It must be admitted, though, that there are a few black sheep among the white ones, destructive rascals that sometimes strike at the very foundations of bird society by robbing the nests of inoffensive neighbors. You might call them Dr. Jekyll and Mr. Hyde characters, for they run their own family affairs on as high a level of decency as anyone could ask.

Crows are noted leaders in this dual personality group. You will often see one of them prowling silently among the trees in May or June, eyes alert for some temporarily unguarded nest. Frequently the black fellow's progress is accompanied by frenzied cries from all the smaller birds, which instinctively know the peril. But too often their outbursts fail to avert the flapping pause, the quick gobbling of eggs or nestling young alike. Crow raids on the vast waterfowl breeding grounds in the far Northwest are seriously destructive, despite the size and defensive strength of the ducks and geese whose nests are victimized.

Blue jays, those noisy, flashily dressed crow cousins, do their share of egg and baby snatching, too, and in much the same manner. The avenging parents that both of these robbers really fear are the indomitable kingbird and the pint-size ruby-throated hummingbird, whose David and Goliath counter-attacks are brilliantly successful.

In those parts of the seacoast region where fish crows are found, these smaller relatives of the common crow also do their share of egg and young bird eating. When you realize that both those big blackbirds, the purple grackle and the boat-tailed grackle, have the same habit, you may wonder if there isn't some connection between dark feathers and dark deeds, but really that's just coincidence.

Oddly enough, one of our cheeriest little dooryard birds, the house wren, sometimes turns egg destroyer, though I have never heard of its eating the contents of the shells into which it sometimes jabs its bill. Maybe it's just mischievousness—a wren would be quite capable of that!

At first thought, it seems strange that in the world of Nature where countless steps are taken to provide for the continuance of the race a few kinds of birds should so cold-bloodedly destroy posterity at its very beginning. The true explanation, probably, is that these acts which seem to us so brutal and uncalled-for are merely a normal part of that incredibly complex system of checks and balances whereby Nature keeps each form of life in its proper place for the general good of all.

Crows like wood thrush eggs and those of other birds

A pintail duck shows the propeller action of a wing stroke

The Facts of Flight

BIRDS ARE THE PERFECT MASTERS
OF AIR-BORNE MOVEMENT

COMPARED WITH man's complicated materials and devices for directed flight, the wings of a bird are marvels of simplicity, effectiveness and power. Operated and controlled solely by their owner's muscles, bones, sinews and nerves, they function perfectly month after month, year after year, often through weather conditions that baffle our modern planes and pilots. Furthermore, they were flying ages before we even dreamed of travelling in any manner except along the ground or on the water or by swinging from tree branch to tree branch.

Examine the superbly streamlined wing of any bird and you will see that it has three sections and three joints, much like those in your own arm. Connecting the first or "upper arm" section with the body is the shoulder joint; next come the elbow joint and "forearm"; and finally the "wrist" and "hand." Each section has its distinctive type of principal feathers, supplemented by smaller ones adjacent to the area where the main quills are anchored. In flight, the inner half of the wing (from shoulder to wrist) provides support-

[19]

ing or lifting power, like a plane's wing, while the "hand" portion, with its longer feathers, is the propeller that moves the bird forward.

All of these sections and joints are controlled by muscles and ligaments that permit a wide range of positions to meet any air condition and every flight maneuver. The area, pitch, angle, shape and directional movement of the wing can be altered instantly and at will. By various combinations of these factors a bird can speed up, slow down, change course, drop, rise almost vertically, stop—even fly backward, in some cases.

When you see a bird in flight its wings appear to be merely flapping up and down. High-speed movie photographs, however, have revealed what really happens. Perhaps the most striking disclosure is that the forward motion of a flying bird results from the thrust of the long primary feathers growing from the "hand" portion of the wing. On the down stroke each of these assumes the twist of a plane's propeller blades and, pressing against the air, actually pushes the wings forward, necessarily followed by the rest of the bird.

In the light of all this, the details of wing-feather construction and placement become doubly interesting. All of the large wing feathers, for example, have tapered, springy, tough and yet incredibly light shafts or quills, equipped with flexible side webs composed of parallel strands each of which has tiny hooks to interlock it with its neighbors. If any of these becomes separated it can be easily rejoined by a stroking motion.

Yes, bird flight is one of the major wonders of our present world. And yet, down to the last detail, it was perfected many, many millions of years ago!

Living Incubators

THEY DATE FROM PREHISTORIC

DAYS BUT STILL WORK

PERFECTLY

IF YOU HAVE ever operated an incubator full of hens' eggs you know how important it is to maintain exactly the right temperatures and humidity for the twenty-one days prior to hatching, not to mention turning the eggs at stated intervals. Even with the best automatic devices, this incubating job is no foolproof matter, yet the wild birds accomplish it with no artificial help.

First, nearly all species build nests with fine, soft inner linings that serve as excellent insulators. In the case of whip-poor-wills, grouse, sea gulls and other ground nesters, the soil itself is such a good temperature stabilizer that nest lining is often omitted. Secondly, a bird's normal body temperature is higher than ours—often by as much as six to eight degrees. This generated heat is well conserved while the eggs are being brooded, for the soft underbody feathers of the old bird, fluffed around the eggs in the center of the nest, form a perfect blanket. The feathers are adjustable, too, like every good thermostat.

And in the third place, all the heat, whether from

body or air, is generated naturally and therefore retains the humidity that is often lacking where artificial heating systems are used.

Turning the eggs, to insure normal development inside the shell, is probably accomplished by all birds with either their bills or feet, although positive evidence on this point is limited to comparatively few species. One of the kinds that we definitely know about is the ring-necked pheasant, which has been photographed while using her bill as an expert egg turner.

Virtually every kind of bird lays more than one egg, the number averaging about four or five and running up to fifteen or eighteen in a few species. Since it is important that every young bird shall have its fair chance to develop normally, all the eggs must hatch at approximately the same time; otherwise, the first youngster out of its shell would be larger than the last and so grab more than its share of food. This simultaneous hatching is arranged perfectly by the old bird's habit of not starting to brood her eggs until she has laid the final one. For some obscure reason, barn owls and occasional other species start sitting on the first egg as soon as it's laid.

The incubation period lasts from ten to sixteen days among our small and medium-size birds, and twenty to twenty-eight with ducks, hawks and most other large kinds. As a rule the female takes over the full assignment, except as her mate may relieve her temporarily while she goes out for a meal. Just to prove that every law has its exception, the male rose-breasted grosbeak not only assumes his full share of egg-sitting, but sings cheerfully to himself while he does it!

A female bob-white covering her eggs is a perfect incubator

*Cooper's hawk and red-winged blackbird, a
lesson in peril*

Why Birds Seem Nervous

THERE'S A REAL REASON, THOUGH
THEY MAY NOT KNOW IT

MOST OF US think of birds as leading care-free, happy lives, doing pretty much as they want to when they want to. It comes as something of a shock to realize that every one of them, except possibly some of the birds of prey and other extra-large kinds, is on the alert every moment of its waking hours to dodge the stroke of sudden death.

If this sounds fantastic, look carefully at the next everyday bird that gives you a good, close view. You will notice that, even though it may be sitting still, it is in a state of obvious nervous tension, its head and eyes constantly twitching this way and that as though it wanted to watch in all directions at once. As a matter of fact, that is precisely what it's trying to do, and the primary motive is to spot and escape from a surprise attack by a cat, hawk, snake, man or some other of the numerous perils to which birds are perpetually exposed. Even when a bird is hunting for food this watchfulness never flags, for fear has top priority over nearly every other emotion or instinct. Probably its closest competitor is that other powerful impulse to defend the eggs or young even in the face of serious personal danger, examples of which are noted elsewhere on these pages.

If we mere human beings lived in such everlasting dread we would probably go hopelessly insane within twenty-four hours. How, then, can the birds stand it—not only stand it, but find the spirit to sing, play and generally enjoy themselves as they so often do?

The answer is that they are nervously and mentally constituted to endure the strain without its wearing them down. Their actions and reactions are far more purely instinctive and automatic than most of ours, and the chances are that they have little or no conscious imagination as we understand the term. I very much doubt if the song sparrow scanning earth and sky every few seconds while he suns himself on a branch of your dooryard lilac has any realization of why he is so watchful, or of what his alertness may disclose. He is merely obeying a subconscious impulse implanted in him by a completely realistic Nature that insists upon eternal vigilance as the price of life.

Once you recognize the existence and power of this basic fear you will understand many of the odd things that birds do. It is the principal reason why virtually all species make real efforts to conceal their nests; why those which come to your winter feeding station are at first so unwilling to visit it before sizing up the situation thoroughly; why sun-basking, apparently relaxed birds suddenly tighten their fluffed feathers and crouch for a fast take-off.

A tragic way to live? Well, yes, in a way. But the birds don't seem to mind it, and maybe that's what really counts, after all.

Slipshod Nest Builders

YOU MIGHT THINK THEY WOULD
USE MORE CARE AGAINST
FATAL ACCIDENTS

GENERALLY SPEAKING, birds' nests are substantial affairs, ingeniously built of natural materials and perfectly adapted to housing eggs and young in safety and comfort until the new generation is old enough to take wing and assume its share of carrying on the family. It is something of a shock to realize that even a small minority of species should be so careless in their nest building that some of their offspring pay the penalty with their lives.

A good example of this occasional sketchy construction is the nest of a mourning dove, the only "wild pigeon" found over most of the United States. It is nothing but a platform made of a few dead sticks loosely crisscrossed on a tree branch or crotch and so carelessly put together that sometimes the two eggs fall through and are smashed on the ground below. Even if this does not happen, the youngsters may tumble over the edge in their early days, thus ending their career before it really starts. Similarly poor building characterizes most of the pigeon tribe, and perhaps is explained by their bills and feet being unsuited to substantial construction work such as other birds do.

Another case is the yellow-billed cuckoo's nest, a loose, flat platform of twigs with a trifle of softer material on top. True, it isn't quite as flimsy as the dove's, but nobody could call it safe and sane.

Again, take the home of a nighthawk family. This isn't really a nest at all, for the two eggs are laid right on bare ground, gravel, the top of a big rock, or even on the flat roof of a building without a single grass blade or bit of down to cushion them. Fortunately, they are quite protectively colored, as is the old bird, whereas the dove's eggs are white. But you can't help wondering why they or the nestlings are not fatally baked by the summer sun.

Most of the common sea birds, such as the gulls and terns, are almost as indifferent to nesting materials as the nighthawk is, for they simply form slight depressions in the loose sand or choose rock crevices possibly cushioned with a few bits of seaweed if they happen to be handy. There seems to be some excuse for their casual system, however, in the fact that the desolate, isolated areas usually chosen for breeding purposes harbor fewer natural enemies than are found in inland regions.

The reasons for these variations from the safety-first habits of most birds? Well, the chances are that the true answers lie hidden somewhere back in those dim ages when birds, like all life, were slowly evolving from few and simpler forms toward the immensely varied species that we know today.

Mourning dove nests are so flimsy that they are unsafe

*Nighthawks consume fantastic numbers of
flying insects*

How Much Do Birds Eat?

FANTASTIC FACTS AND FIGURES
ON YOUNG AND OLD

EVERYONE KNOWS that babies have to be fed so often that it's tough on their parents, but the old folks who really earn the right to be worn out by the duties of keeping their offspring's tummies filled are the birds. Believe it or not, accepted records show that a pair of purple martins may bring food home to their youngsters as many as 312 times in a single day and rose-breasted grosbeaks 426 times, while house wrens are the probable winners of the endurance prize with no less than 600 nourishment-bearing trips to the nest between dawn and dark. As to what this sort of thing means in actual food quantity, there is the typical case of a single nestling robin that is known to have swallowed from fifty to seventy cutworms daily for a period of seventeen days.

Nor are these exceptional figures; the strong probabilities are that numerous other common birds are just as busily engaged. Small wonder that the young of many species, gulping down at least their own weight in food every twenty-four hours, increase their heftiness anywhere from 20 to 60 per cent during the same period. Clearly, the diet suits them perfectly.

There are very practical reasons for such feverish activity by both parents and offspring. For one thing, most of the food brought to young birds consists of insects, which contain considerable waste matter along with their nutritive properties. Also, the whole digestive system of a bird, regardless of age, functions extremely fast and therefore needs frequent refilling. But added to all this is the urgency of the growth schedule which seeks to get the young ones out of the helpless and therefore perilous stage as soon as possible, and fit them to fend for themselves. Actually, many kinds of birds are able to fly and gather much of their own food in two or three weeks after they leave the egg.

As a matter of fact, the habit of eating as much as possible and at frequent intervals follows a bird throughout its life. If you can stand a few more statistics for a moment, consider these authentic figures, representing the stomach contents of single adult birds at the time of examination: flicker, 5,040 ants; purple grackle, 13 crayfish; bob-white, 10,000 pigweed seeds; yellow-billed cuckoo, 23 tent caterpillars (at 6 A.M.!); nighthawk, 500 mosquitoes; ground dove, 1,600 purslane seeds; nighthawk again, 2,175 flying ants.

And that's not all of it, for these are only *single-meal* counts. When you consider that most birds continue eating more or less all day, the total amounts they get away with must be staggering. Clearly, all that we hear and read about the economic value of birds to mankind has a solid basis of truth behind it. The argument that their consumption of fruits and grains used by human beings counteracts the good they do is of little weight in the overall picture.

Feathered Camouflage

OR HOW TO KEEP YOUR
ENEMIES FROM SEEING YOU

MANY, MANY thousands of years before World War I spread the meaning of the word "camouflage" around the globe, birds and animals were perfectly demonstrating the principles of protective markings and coloration to keep their enemies from noticing them. When we human beings picked up the idea for our own purposes it was already older than Noah's Ark.

Nearly every bird you see is an object lesson in this method of self-effacement. You will notice that the upper and side parts are darker than the lower and, especially in the case of sparrows, meadowlarks and other species that live mostly on the ground, are colored and patterned in rough imitation of the soil and its surface covering of dead leaves, twigs, withered grasses and other litter. The comparative lightness of breast and belly has the effect of modifying the shadow which normally covers a bird's underbody even when its owner is in full sunlight, and thus serves to make it less conspicuous. The majority of birds that spend most of their time up among the trees lack this variety of pattern on backs and wings, and their colors run more toward soft greens and grays that will harmonize with their surroundings. And many of the sea birds, like gulls and terns, are quite uniformly blue-gray on top, with touches of black and white here and there, to make them less noticeable from above when they are floating on open water.

This concealment system is invaluable at all times, but it becomes almost a must during the breeding season when the old birds are brooding their eggs or keeping the newly hatched youngsters warm. These duties fall chiefly on the mother bird, and you will notice that in those species where the sexes are differently colored she wears a more perfect camouflage suit than her mate. Furthermore, with very few exceptions, fledgling birds are even more obscurely marked than their parents, presumably to conceal them while the old birds are out foraging for food.

There are exceptions to all rules, of course, even to this one of protective coloration. Nothing could be more noticeable, for instance, than the brilliancy of a male scarlet tanager or Baltimore oriole, or the jet black of a crow. In the case of gorgeously colored species it has been suggested that ages ago they may have been tropic dwellers only, clothed to harmonize with the large and often flamboyant flowers around them, but no such explanation fits the sable feathers of crows or ravens, whose extreme wariness may enable them to dispense with color protection. Be that as it may, the fact remains that bird life is full of apparent inconsistencies, to many of which we have not yet found the answers.

[34]

765881

Protective coloration hides this woodcock on her nest

Crested flycatchers like snake skins for nest material

[36]

Queer Building Materials

SOME BIRDS ARE AS
ORIGINAL IN NESTING
AS IN APPEARANCE

SOME YEARS AGO a wood thrush nest was found with a scrap from a local newspaper's "Houses for Rent" column carefully worked into its outer wall. Merely an amusing coincidence, of course, and yet it pointed up a known fact: the strangeness of the materials which birds sometimes use in building the family home.

Bits of soft paper are often commandeered by robins for this purpose, and they and several others of the thrush family customarily gather beakfuls of mud to serve as mortar for cementing the collections of plant stems, grasses, shreds of inner bark and other soft stuff which are the chief components of their nests. Both barn and cave swallows utilize mud still more freely—in fact, a good deal of the nest is made of it, though there is a fine grass and feather lining; the cliff swallow omits even this cushion. Phoebes also use mud bonded with moss, and do such a good masonry job that one of their dwellings may last several years if rain and snow cannot reach it.

A mystifying oddity is the cast-off snake skin which

[37]

the crested flycatcher frequently weaves into its nest tucked away in a convenient tree cavity. There is a popular belief that this is a sort of charm to keep living snakes away, but there is no real basis for such a theory. Nowadays the cresteds often take advantage of our manufacturing know-how by substituting strips of cellophane, waxed paper and other materials with a nice snakeskin glitter.

Wild geese and some other waterfowl have a curious habit of plucking out their own breast feathers to build soft, warm linings for their nests. Baltimore orioles, for their part, are delighted when they find bits of soft string or yarn which they can work into their marvelously woven pouchlike nests—preferring light and neutral colors to dark ones, incidentally, perhaps because these fit better into the pale gray scheme which they have followed for ages.

Spider silk, lichens and old caterpillar cocoons are utilized by hummingbirds, vireos and several other tree-nesting birds in finishing the outsides of their homes, not as decorations, but for camouflage. Again, hummers and many other small species gather various plant downs to provide extra-soft beds for their wee eggs and offspring.

Entirely different material and a unique technique are a habit with the chimney swift, that superb flier and abundant summer resident through the United States as far west as the Rockies. Breaking off small dead twigs by flying against them, the swift carries them into unused chimneys where they are cemented against the vertical walls, and to each other, with a gluelike saliva secreted by glands in the builders' mouths—one of the bird world's strangest procedures.

The Flying Patrol

HAVE YOU EVER realized that the world's birds constitute a huge police force charged with the duty of helping to maintain a balance between all the forms of life? Tens of billions strong, their operatives reach into every corner of the land and over all the network of the waters. Plants, fish, animals, insects, reptiles, men—every group we know—depend in part upon the efficiency with which the birds carry out their assignment. Without them, unthinkable chaos would engulf the globe.

Yes, it is an incredible organization, fantastic in its vastness and complexity. Yet from your own kitchen window, along every roadside, across the fields, you can see at least some of its members, each demonstrating the specialized equipment to carry on its task.

Take the sparrows and finches, with their short, strong but dexterous bills made to order for gathering and eating the small seeds of the weeds which otherwise might overrun the land. Or a woodpecker, clinging with strong, spread-toe feet to the trunk of a tree while it whangs away with chisel bill to reach some

[39]

grub boring in the wood; notice how those pointed, stiffened tail feathers are pressed against the bark to help support the body weight and provide a firm stance for the delivery of the blows. By contrast, notice the slender, needle-sharp bills of the warblers, perfect for snatching aphids and other small, weak insect forms from leaves and twigs, and the agility with which their owners skip about in the shrubs and trees after their prey. Or a phoebe or kingbird doing sentry duty on a wire or dead branch from which it can take off instantly in pursuit of some air-borne bug and, literally on the fly, snap and crush it in that long, broad-based bill which so seldom misses its mark.

And then there are the swallows and chimney swifts, patrolling the skies during the hours of daylight, darting this way and that after high-flying insects and trapping them in opened mouths so relatively huge that they look like caverns. And the heron group, long-necked and spear-billed for the harpooning of unwary fish, frogs and the like; theirs is a watery hunting ground, and so their legs are stiltlike to hold them high while their feet are exceptionally large in order to find sufficient support in the oozy mud and marshes. Again, the talon claws and powerful hooked beaks of hawks and owls are perfect for capturing and devouring small animals like rats and mice, and so these birds of prey are enormously valuable in keeping the rodent population within bounds.

These are but a few out of a multitude of special adaptations that exist all about us. There is no more fascinating pathway to follow in the whole field of bird study.

Tent caterpillars are tidbits to a yellow-billed cuckoo

Robins have a reason for singing, but it's an odd one

Why Do Birds Sing?

YOU'D NEVER GUESS

THE REAL REASON

FOR THEIR MUSIC

WHAT IS IT? Does the springtime robin, perched atop the big maple on the lawn, pour out that rich, full-throated warble just because he likes the sound of it? Is he trying to attract a potential wife or cheer up an acquired one? Can his song be simply the audible expression of high spirits and enjoyment of life in general?

These are perfectly natural and plausible questions, but people who have studied birds for many years believe that none of them can be answered with an unqualified "yes." The chief motive, in the opinion of leading ornithologists, is to warn all other males of the same species to keep their distance. All other reasons, these authorities believe, are either temporary or relatively unimportant. This may sound a bit preposterous, but let's look at the facts.

In the first place, only the males sing, and practically all of their singing for the year is done shortly before and during the breeding season. Each one of them is at least a probable father of a dependent family, and that family can grow up successfully only if it is provided constantly with plenty of food of the right kind and at the right stage in its development.

Only an area of some size can produce enough bird food—certain insects, worms, grubs, seeds and such—to support a single pair and their young properly. If another family of the same kind should start poaching on it the competition might be serious for the original settlers. So, by one of those unbelievable regulations (followed instinctively, by the way) which govern all forms of wildlife, the total supply of food is allotted so that everybody gets his fair share *if he stays on the job and plays the game according to the rules that have been laid down for him.*

That sounds reasonable enough for the robin singing in the rain, or for any other particular species of bird you want to take as an example. But how about the male song sparrow or catbird or wren that bubbles so ecstatically from the shrubbery right beside the maple and often sets up housekeeping within a few yards of where the robin's family lives? Isn't he an important rival for the food supply? Yes, at first thought he is, but here's the catch:

Another of those basic regulations I mentioned provides that different kinds of birds shall eat different kinds of food. Some subsist chiefly on seeds, some on ants, some on flying insects, some on worms and berries, and so on up and down the line. Almost any kind and size of area you care to name contains a variety of different foods and therefore can support a variety of birds. The saturation point for any one species is not the saturation point for all.

How Nests Are Built

BIRDS HAVE exactly three tools with which to construct their nests: feet, bills and bodies. With that meager equipment they contrive an astonishing variety of structures, some cut out of solid wood, others woven into almost fabriclike texture, still others built of crude masonry or, in the case of eagles and ospreys, of crisscrossed sticks so large and numerous that the completed nests weigh several hundred pounds. The full story of these feathered artisans' ingenuity and deftness is far too long for these pages, but here are a few examples that will serve by way of illustration.

A female robin begins by selecting a substantial support such as the crotch of a tree, a stout forking branch, or the top of a barn beam or similar spot. Here she assembles beakfuls of dead grasses, twigs and stems, shaping them into a rough cup by squatting and pivoting while she tweaks them against her body. To this foundation she brings mud and more grass to bond it, molding the mixture against her breast as she continues pivoting. In one to several days she has completed the extra-soft, mudless lining and has a firm, warm receptacle for her eggs which exactly fits her body as she broods them.

Baltimore orioles employ a different technique. Their home site includes several strong twigs over which the bird first hangs long strands of vegetal or tree bark fiber, string and so on. These she fastens in place, then connects them by a combined weaving and looping procedure until, in three or four days, the pouch is ready for its inner lining.

Woodpeckers gather no special materials, but merely chop out cavities in dead trees, and leave some of the chips as bedding in the bottom of the holes. For this tough task they use nothing but their straight, chisel-like bills mounted on skulls specially designed to withstand the shock of repeated blows. Split open an abandoned woodpecker nest, and you will be astonished by its uniformity and the even pattern of its walls. It seems inconceivable that any bird's bill could accomplish so much so skillfully.

Behind these and many other nest-building marvels lies a further surprise: practically all individuals of each species, though they may be distributed from coast to coast, build identical nests in the same manner. Do they teach each other? Is it just a matter of copying? No, nothing like that. The incredible truth is that every robin, every sparrow and duck, hawk and heron and hummingbird, hatches from its egg with all the latent instincts necessary to follow each rule laid down for its breed under the Big Plan, when the time comes for it to play its allotted part in the game of life.

The cliff swallow builds a queer nest with mud or clay

x

[47]

A yellow-bellied sapsucker visits his little feeding wells

Odd Feeding Habits

SOME BIRDS ARE AS ORIGINAL
IN THEIR WAYS AS ANY PERSON

MOST BIRDS eat their meals in the ordinary way; that is, they pick up the food in their bills, juggle or crush it a bit if it is large or tough, and swallow it on the spot. But now and then you find species whose table manners are extraordinary.

Consider, for instance, the herring gull, commonest of its tribe along the Atlantic coast. Actually it is an all-around scavenger, but also a fresh clam addict. No gull can pry open the heavy armor of this shellfish, so the herring gull simply takes the whole thing in its bill, flies thirty feet or so into the air, and drops it so that it smashes open on the rocks or, if a concrete road is near by, on that more efficient surface. Ravens practice a similar technique, which they may have figured out for themselves rather than learning it from the gulls.

You naturally expect odd things from a humming-bird, but many people do not know that, along with sipping nectar from flowers, it takes in many tiny insects attracted by the same sweet liquid. Also, a hummer is a skilled catcher of small flying insects, snatching them out of the air as deftly as any phoebe or kingbird. And speaking of phoebes and other regular flycatchers, they perch in exposed places so as to get better views of their meals on wings!

A standard habit of the yellow-bellied sapsucker suggests the hummingbird system, with modifications. This odd woodpecker drills rows of small holes in living trees, eats some of the soft inner bark, and returns to them at intervals to feast on the collected sap and the insects it attracts. Sometimes the contents of the little wells ferment to the point where the hungry sapsuckers become actually intoxicated.

Shrikes, innocent in appearance but implacable destroyers of mice, big grasshoppers, small birds and so on, often skewer their victims in thorny trees or on the spikes of barbed-wire fences. This probably simplifies the job of tearing them into eatable pieces, but often the game simply hangs there until its captor works up a fresh appetite. Naturally, such procedure gave rise to the shrike's other name of butcher-bird, by which it is known to country people in many parts of its range.

Storage of food for future use is practiced by several other birds. Chickadees and white-breasted nuthatches tuck sunflower seeds into tree bark crevices against a hungry day, and the latter bird does so with acorns and beechnuts as well—hence its name. Most kinds of jays are hoarders, too, specializing in acorns poked into crannies. And the California woodpecker goes them one better by drilling many holes of exactly the right size in dead trees or thick bark and stuffing each one with a single acorn, point-first so that the soft cap end can be easily opened when the time comes!

Whole Towns of Birds

SOME KINDS SEEM TO PREFER
CROWDED TENEMENT LIFE

THE DETERMINATION of most birds to raise their annual families in strict privacy so far as others of their own kind are concerned, while a comparatively small number of different species are just as addicted to community life, is a first-class puzzle until you begin looking into the reasons behind it. Then, suddenly, it becomes as clear as daylight.

A primary cause lies in the feeding habits of the species involved. Near-home feeders like catbirds and bluebirds are solitary nesters because there might not be enough of their favorite food to go around if others of their kind set up housekeeping near by. But swallows, chimney swifts, herons and most of the sea birds range far and wide in search of their daily bread, sometimes covering hundreds of miles between sunrise and sunset. Colony nesting has no drawbacks for them from the food angle, and presumably presents some advantages that we do not fully understand.

Among our fairly common land birds, purple martins are probably the most striking of the colony nesters. As many as two dozen pairs of these large economy-size swallows sometimes pack their families into a single multiple-room house built especially for them and mounted on a tall pole. When the nesting season is in full swing the chattering and gossiping of the birds reminds you for all the world of a crowded city tenement, but few real quarrels seem to develop. Community spirit is so strong that the whole gang will attack any intruder that may look dangerous and speedily put him to flight. Barn, cliff, cave and bank swallows have much the same sort of colonizing spirit, though they choose different places to demonstrate it: the first in and around old country barns and houses; the second and third on cliffs and in caves; and the last in sandy, steep banks where each pair excavates a tunnel in which to build its nest.

The real bird towns are the "rookeries" of the herons, sea gulls, terns and other waterside or seafaring species. These breeding communities sometimes contain twenty or thirty thousand adults, and perhaps an equal number of youngsters. In the case of sea birds, especially, the nests may be literally within reaching distance of each other, yet there is little fighting. About the only roughness shown is when a young bird mistakes somebody else's parent for its own and becomes too insistent in its demands for food. A sharp and sometimes fatal peck quickly puts an end to that, for apparently each old bird recognizes its own child and objects to feeding its neighbor's.

These bird communities, regardless of their size, are occupied for many years by the same birds and their descendants, unless serious changes occur. Certain of the sea birds travel thousands of miles each year to return to them as nesting time approaches.

[52]

Like most herons, the great blue often nests in colonies

[53]

The wings of golden-eye ducks are famous whistlers

On Whistling Wings

IT IS INDIVIDUAL FEATHERS
THAT MAKE THE SOUND

A FEW BIRDS, like the owls, fly with no audible sound from their wings. The majority of other kinds produce a definite air disturbance that ranges from the faintest whisper to a loud whirr in the case of such sorts as bob-whites and grouse. And a select few give out a tremulous whistle as they shoot through the air with characteristically rapid strokes.

If you are familiar with the woodcock, that grotesque yet beautiful member of the snipe clan that feeds at night by probing in damp or mucky soil, you know the thin, tremulous whistles with which it darts away through the woods when you startle it from its daylight siesta on the ground. Were you to examine its wings carefully you would find that the three outer primary feathers are shorter and much narrower than the rest, besides having an odd curve in their rear webs. The theory is that when these feathers are extended and driven forcefully through the air they cause a characteristic whistling noise, somewhat as a skilled swordsman is said to make his blade "whistle."

The mourning dove is another excellent whistler

when in flight, and here again we find the outer primaries pointed and relatively narrow. The wing-beat is very rapid, particularly at the take-off, as is the woodcock's. Quite possibly the speed with which these end feathers are whipped through the air has a bearing on the sound that they produce. Naturally, a wing stroke being what it is, the outer portion moves faster than that nearer the body.

Most ducks flap their wings so rapidly when in flight that they almost flicker, a habit that is necessary to keep their relatively heavy bodies on their course. Only strong flight feathers can stand up under such pressure, so those of a duck are stiff, quite narrow and pointed, especially those at the outer end of the wing. As a result, the wings of all flying ducks whistle to a certain extent. In the case of the American golden-eye, one of our hardy salt-water species, this sound is so loud and clear that many hunters call the bird "whistler."

In high ornithological circles there is some argument over whether the flight-whistle of certain species, including woodcock and Wilson's snipe, is made by the wings or is a vocal production. Positive proof on either side is difficult to produce, but thus far the wing theory seems to have the best backing. I doubt if there is any valid disagreement with the belief that feathers are responsible as far as ducks are concerned. Surely, no duck's voice could produce the soft, sweet whistling that drifts down through the quiet dusk from a flock of golden-eyes or blacks sweeping high overhead as they wing their way to find some secluded resting place where they can spend the night in comfort and security.

[56]

Courtship Show-offs

MUTUAL ADMIRATION IS
A FACTOR IN BIRD
MARRIAGES, TOO

PICK OUT ALMOST ANY form of animate life you please, from fish and frogs up the line to man, and you'll find that there is a good bit of the show-off spirit in the males, especially when it comes to impressing the women-folks. Sometimes it seems like plain bluff, or perhaps an attempt to conceal some weakness. But the chances are a good deal better than even that the underlying cause is really biological: the age-old instinct to impress a potential mate.

Birds are no exception to this all but universal trait. Every male shows it to some extent in the prenesting season, and some carry it to fantastic lengths. Thus, the amusingly self-possessed little white-breasted nuthatch puts on a real courtship show of his black, white and blue-gray markings by spreading wings and tail and tilting slowly back and forth as proudly as any peacock. Flickers pose their heads this way and that, turn, twist, flutter and use every trick to display their handsome plumage, accompanying the performance with throaty notes as though to call attention to especially beautiful markings. Apparently they sometimes overdo the job, for occasionally an extra female appears on the scene and there's considerable feminine rowing over which one shall finally have the gentleman in the case.

The bobolink does a sort of double show-off act at mating time, singing madly as he chases a female through the air and, when she alights on the ground, parading stiffly around her with buff neck feathers raised like a ruff, wings half spread and tail dragging. A similar trick of feather display is the trump card of the red-winged blackbird, whose scarlet epaulettes edged with buff are startlingly dramatic against his jet black coat when he spreads them wide and bows ceremoniously before his lady friend.

That peppery midget, the ruby-throated humming-bird, has his own individual way of love-making, as you might expect. While the more soberly dressed female perches quietly on a twig, her suitor swings back and forth at terrific speed through the arc of a fifty-foot circle as if he were the weight on the end of a gigantic pendulum. It is a breath-taking performance to watch, but the squeaky little jabbering that accompanies it proves that the hummer, at least, has everything under excellent control.

And so it goes, with species after species. Usually it is the male that dominates the stage, but if you should ever see a mockingbird courtship with its ceremonial act in which both birds face each other with heads and tails held high and solemnly circle and reverse like old-time court dancers, you'll realize that some lady birds, too, have a knack for showing off and making it pay.

A courting redwing displays his epaulets with pride

[59]

*An unknown power enables dowitchers to
fly in unison*

Pass the Word Along

BIRDS CAN AND DO
COMMUNICATE, AND
NOT ONLY BY VOICE

ORDINARILY we think of birds as using their voices to express their own passing emotions— fear, hunger, exuberance, defiance and so on —rather than as a means of communicating with each other. There can be no question about the first half of this belief, but further consideration will disclose plenty of evidence that the second just does not follow. Take the case of the crow, for example.

Crows have an unmistakable language of their own and use it in conversations much as people do. By varying the pitch, length, number and timing of their calls they send out warnings, issue orders, summon help, express fear, anger and satisfaction, and often chat with each other in what sounds like regular back-fence gossip. I doubt if a crow is ever at a loss for words to tell all its relatives within hearing distance just what it thinks, sees, plans and decides is the best thing to do.

Blue jays have a similar ability, though it is not so highly developed for long-range use. As if to compensate for any vocabulary shortage, they are masters of voice control and can murmur just as easily as they scream. For strictly family purposes, too, blue jays have a special language as intriguing as it is low and musical. You hear it especially in late summer when the youngsters are fully at home on the wing and following their parents on endless explorations among the treetops in search of food.

Another clear-cut illustration of effective speaking is the rallying call of a covey of bob-whites that has been scattered by hunters. It is one of the sweetest sounds in birddom, a vibrant yet plaintive *whoi-lee, whoi-lee,* echoed by bird after bird as its fright abates and the flock draws together once more.

Every species, as a matter of fact, can communicate at least some elemental information by vocal means, and many of its alarm notes appear to be understood by other kinds. And when birds are migrating at night you can hear, if the weather is favorable and your ears are sharp, many chips and lisps and faint whistles not used by day—signals of encouragement and guidance, perhaps, along the darkened skyways.

All these instances of audible communication are understandable enough, but what about the astounding, instantaneous precision with which a hundred flying starlings, shorebirds, blackbirds or other tight-flocking species wheel and veer and dive as a single unit? No single note is sounded, so far as we know, nor is there any positive proof of how the word is passed along. The most plausible explanation is that the flawless unity of movement arises from some sort of thought transference—a sixth sense, if you will—as mysterious as it is effective.

Bills and Tongues

THEY ARE AMAZINGLY VARIED, YET EACH KIND DOES ITS WORK EFFICIENTLY

A BIRD'S BILL is an excellent clue to the family to which its owner belongs, but that is only one of the many interesting facts that it discloses. Once you start putting two and two together, as it were, you gain fresh viewpoints on bird life as vital as they are revealing.

Bills and the tongues inside them are far more varied than many people realize, and there are always valid reasons for their differences. Thus, the slender, sharply pointed beaks of the wood warblers are perfectly adapted to snatching with the precision of a surgeon's forceps the small insects, caterpillars and little bugs in general that constitute the warblers' principal diet. So, too, with flycatcher bills—stronger, slightly hooked at the tip and broader at the base, the better to grip, crush and swallow the larger flying insects on which they feed. Sparrows, on the other hand, are primarily seed eaters with a sprinkling of bugs on the side; consequently their bills are relatively short and heavy for seed-crushing power, yet sharply pointed and adroit to pick up very small items. All the birds of prey, of course, have powerful hooked beaks for tearing the flesh of their prey into eatable shreds, while woodpecker bills are straight and chisel-pointed for wood chopping that will enable them to reach borers that live sometimes an inch or so beneath the bark.

Few birds are more specialized in their feeding habits than the several hundred species of hummingbirds whose amazingly long, thin bills are so ideally designed for probing into flowers. And of course the broad, rather flattened bills of many wild duck species, equipped as they are with rows of little serrations along their edges, make perfect tools for straining little aquatic creatures out of the mud and sand in which this favorite food is found.

Along with these and many other bill types go tongues whose shapes and sizes are equally distinctive and always competent for the second stage of speeding fresh-caught food on its way to the stomach. If you have watched a parrot cracking a sunflower seed you know the part its tongue plays in "spitting out" the shell and chaff so the kernel can be swallowed clean. Seed-eating wild birds do the same sort of thing, and so their tongues are deft and extremely busy at meal time. On the other hand, a woodpecker has a spear-pointed, barbed and amazingly extensible tongue wherewith to skewer and pull into the mouth those luckless grubs whose homes have been broken into by the bill's hammer blows. One of the woodpecker group, the flicker, also uses its long tongue to great advantage in pulling ants out of their earth burrows.

Yes, the subject of bird beaks and tongues could well fill a whole book. And many chapters of it can be read right in your own back yard.

Hummingbird bills are examples of special adaptation

Most hole-nesters, like hairy woodpeckers, lay white eggs

Eggs of Many Colors

THEY ARE AS VARIED AND
LOVELY AS THE BIRDS
THAT LAY THEM

WE ARE ALL FAMILIAR with that delightful hue known as robin's-egg blue, but it is no more than an introduction to the incredible variety and beauty of the colors and patterns to be found on the egg-shells of nearly all our everyday wild birds. Some are pure white, others a single, solid color like the robin's. Then there are innumerable shades and tints of brown, green, blue, lavender, pink, red, purple and yellow, blended and intermixed as backgrounds, blotches, thin lines, dots and streaks until you wonder how so many effects could have been created. Each species has its distinctive style, but even among only four or five eggs laid by a single mother bird there are often slight variations in the color distribution that give each one its own individuality.

All these colors come from special ducts and are deposited in and on the shell while it is being formed inside the bird shortly before the completed egg is laid. Astonishing though this may seem, it becomes almost unbelievable when you recall that many birds lay an egg a day for a week or even longer, and that the color ducts must repeat their artistic performance on each one.

It is probable that in the beginning, when birds were evolving from their reptilian ancestors, all eggs were white-shelled; those of our present snakes, as you know, are still white. But as bird types and species gradually developed and acquired the habit of building open nests rather than the earth-hidden ones of the reptiles, various colors and markings were added to make the eggs less visible to predators during the intervals when the old birds were not brooding them. Here again was the principle of protective coloration, so vital in the lives of wild creatures down through the ages.

But, you say, the eggs of woodpeckers, martins and mourning doves are pure white, with no trace of camouflage. True, but consider this: the first two nest in cavities which provide almost perfect concealment, so there is no need for protective coloring. And as for the doves, whose flimsy nests lack this visual protection, the males and females divide the incubation duties so closely that there is virtually no moment when the eggs are not completely hidden under their bodies.

This whole subject of bird eggs is deeply interesting and well worth looking into more fully at any of the better natural history museums when you have an opportunity. It has its practical side, too, for if you are familiar with the more common kinds they often serve as excellent clues to the ownership of many nests that you come across in the course of your bird-watching prowlings.

Home Defense

BIRDS MAY NOT LOOK
HEROIC, BUT THEY
VERY OFTEN ARE

GUARDING THE SAFETY of eggs and young is a primary instinct common to all birds, for without it the future of the race would be dubious indeed. Concealment of the nest, secretiveness in approaching and leaving it, devotion to every duty of parenthood regardless of difficulties—these are a few of its less obvious but highly important evidences. Far more impressive are the protective actions of the old birds after the hatching of their young initiates the climax stage of the family defense impulse.

Few of our everyday species carry their guardianship to the point of physically striking a human being. Indeed, by personal experience I know of only one, and that is the little screech owl which, under cover of early summer darkness, not infrequently claws the heads of passers-by whom it deems dangerous to inexperienced owlets. But almost every kind of bird will carry its defense excitement far enough to endanger its own life, and that takes courage!

Examples of such reckless devotion to the young family's safety are frequent during the nesting season.

You can follow the course of a cat prowling through a bit of woods or brush-land by the frantic cries of alarm and anger from the throats of half the birds in the neighborhood. If you can get close enough to watch what's going on you will notice that the degree of excitement among the different birds varies considerably, and perhaps that two of them are particularly bold in their dives at the marauder, often coming within range of a quick cat leap with extended claws. These usually are the pair whose nest is nearest the scene and therefore in the gravest danger.

Kingbirds and scissor-tailed flycatchers show the same sort of courage in their vicious attacks on far larger crows and hawks, described elsewhere in these pages. Only their amazing agility saves them from a fatal clutch by the powerful beak or feet of the big bird, for frequently the pursuers come into actual physical contact with their enemy.

Right in your own dooryard, any day during the nesting season, you are likely to be the object of frantic bird courage prompted by this instinct to safeguard the younger generation that is still unable to save itself. The hysterical robin that swoops around you almost within arm's length, chattering its objections; the song sparrow feigning injury a few feet away; the irate catbird, crest erect and tail spread, screaming its anger almost in your ears to drive you away from the lilac bush where its nest is hidden— these are unheralded heroics in the family cause, for though the old birds know that you are a hundred times more powerful and potentially dangerous than they, the risk to their own lives is always accepted.

*A Canada goose defending her nest is a
dangerous fighter*

[71]

*Many a Blackburnian warbler flies from
South America to Canada*

Perils of the Flyways

MIGRATION TAKES A HEAVY

TOLL IN UNSUSPECTED WAYS

THE THOUGHT of countless birds, many of them no longer than your hand, flying hundreds or thousands of miles each year in their migrations between North and South is fantastic enough in itself. But how much more thrilling it becomes when you realize that most of their journeying is done at night with only instinct and perhaps the stars to guide them, and that the way is beset with many grave dangers.

The worst perils of the flyways are not the obvious ones such as the talons of predatory hawks and the guns of hunters. The smaller and weaker species avoid these by travelling only after dark, leaving daylight migration largely to the waterfowl and other big, rugged fellows and to certain very swift fliers such as the swallows. But this is a little like stepping out of the frying-pan into the fire, for night brings its own special risks, most of them involved with the weather.

Imagine the helplessness of a warbler or wren overtaken a quarter-mile above the earth by a midnight thunderstorm or other sudden, violent wind. Unable to see the ground below, it must choose between a blind landing which may prove to be on a large lake or in the heart of a great city, and abandoning itself to the buffeting of the gale, which may be still more disastrous. Even if it survives the latter alternative, daylight may find it blown so far off course that return, in its weary, battered condition, may be next to impossible. The number of coastwise migrating birds that are carried out to sea and drowned under such circumstances is unknown, but conceivably it can be very great.

Also there is the peril of fog and the many, many collisions with man-made objects which it entails. Birds instinctively drop closer to the earth when visibility becomes poor, and then, unable to see where they are going, frequently fly into telegraph wires or against tall buildings and are killed or critically injured. Strong artificial lights have a fatal attraction for them in such bad weather; perhaps they think the glow shining through the murk is coming from the sun. One September morning after a night when dense fog had crept in unexpectedly from the sea I climbed the stairway to the top of Fire Island lighthouse, one of the tallest on the Atlantic Coast, and found nearly a hundred birds of different kinds on the cat-walk below the great reflectors, all dead from crashing head-on into the glass.

There is no sure safeguard against these tragedies, but Nature herself has provided a partial one by seeing to it that the heaviest night movements of the migration seasons are launched only on clear, calm evenings when treacherous weather along the route is unlikely to develop.

They Pretend to Be Hurt

DECEPTION CAN PAY OFF
HANDSOMELY WHEN
USED WITH BOLDNESS

EVERY NOW AND THEN you come upon instances of bird behavior that are hard to understand except by the theory that they are the result of a high degree of intelligence and individual planning. Long and expert study of bird mentality, however, indicates that actions and reactions are chiefly instinctive and have little if any relation to conscious thinking as we understand the term. Accepting this belief, the following situations become doubly interesting.

If you should happen to surprise a female ruffed grouse with a brood of newly hatched young the chances are that you will be mystified by her behavior. Instead of whirring away through the springtime woods in her usual manner she is likely to struggle around on the ground in apparent distress, giving every evidence of having a badly injured wing or legs. Try to catch her, and she will somehow manage to keep just out of reach, flopping away pitifully when you think she's almost yours. Follow slowly, and she will wait for you to catch up; hasten your steps, and she will speed up her progress. Finally, having led you to what she considers a safe distance from her hiding children, her injuries miraculously vanish and she roars away in headlong flight.

A similar trick of piteous make-believe is practiced by whip-poor-wills and their larger cousins the nighthawks. Each of these species, however, adds extra frills of its own. The whip-poor-will gives its floppings and tumblings still greater realism by uttering queer whining cries that could mean almost any emotion from worry to extreme pain. But the nighthawk is likely to precede the injury pretense by direct frontal attack with wide-open mouth and threatening hisses, turning to the subtler technique only as a last resort.

No strategy of deception could be more cleverly conceived and executed than this assumption of feigned injuries. One of its prime advantages is that it works equally well with man, fox, snake or any other enemy. No doubt it would be less successful if the young birds disclosed their whereabouts by moving while the show was being staged, but they never budge. The whole performance is as fine an example of family unity and cooperation as you will find in many a day.

This sort of ruse is especially frequent among species that nest on or near the ground, for its maximum realism can be developed only on terra firma. You can never be sure, though, that some non-ground bird will not try it on occasion, for there are few set rules in matters of this sort. Interestingly enough, the trick is played primarily by the females, whose direct parental instinct seems to be more strongly developed than that of the males and in some respects is perhaps more subtle than theirs.

The pretended injury role, as played by a
mother killdeer

Owls must turn their heads in order to move their eyes

Wise Old Owls

THEIR MANNERS ARE AS
ODD AS THEIR LOOKS, BUT
THERE'S ALWAYS A PURPOSE

THOUGH the actual wisdom of owls as compared with other birds is a debatable point, there is no question about their looking as if they knew a great deal more than their neighbors. Perhaps the fact that they have some very strange physical characteristics and are usually more active in darkness than in daylight has had something to do with building up their popular reputation for super-intelligence.

For one thing, an owl's eyes are extra-large and are fixed almost immovably in their sockets, with the result that in order to look up, down or sideways the bird has to move its whole head. This led to that whimsical tale about wringing an owl's neck by walking around him while he twists his head off keeping an eye on you. Actually the head *can* make almost a complete circle, but when its limit is reached the bird flicks it around in the opposite direction so fast that you can hardly see the motion and may not realize that you are being stared at over the other shoulder, so to speak. Incidentally, the extreme size of an owl's eyes and its exceptionally large ear openings give their owner that power of sight and hearing which is so essential in the bird's nocturnal way of life.

Equally distinctive is the odd character of the plumage, especially that of the wings. As compared with other birds, owl feathers are exceptionally soft and muffled with innumerable tiny filaments that deaden all sound and give the bird an absolutely noiseless flight. Such silence is a priceless asset when it comes to slipping up unawares over a night-roaming mouse or rat and clutching it unerringly with eight powerful talons.

Owls swallow their prey bones, fur, feathers and all, either whole or in large chunks, depending on its size. Only the flesh and other soft parts are digested, of course, so the remainder is disposed of by ejecting it through the throat and mouth in the form of long, compact and surprisingly neat pellets. Often you can find these oddities lying under a tree—evergreen, perhaps—in which an owl has spent the day half asleep. Many of them show clearly that they are composed of a mass of hair and little bones. Crumble one, and there's a good chance that you will come upon the perfect, wee skull or jaw of a mouse.

There are fourteen owl species native in the United States, ranging in size from the six-inch elf owl of the Southwest to the giant snowy owl, with its five-foot wing spread, that comes down from the Far North during occasional winters when its food supply up there runs short. And every one of them, in its own owlish way, is as original as something out of Grimm's Fairy Tales.

Family Safety

BIRDS ALWAYS HAVE A
REASON, AND IT'S USUALLY
A GOOD ONE

IT MAY NOT have occurred to you at the time, but if you ever saw a Baltimore oriole's nest swaying at the very tip of a slender, drooping elm branch you were witnessing a perfect example of that resourceful instinct which all birds have for insuring the safety of their expected offspring. I'll admit that such a wind-tossed building site looks downright risky, but consider for a moment. A snake, squirrel or cat looking for a free meal could never reach an oriole's nest, and its place among the elm's leaves screens it from marauding crows. Also, the woven pouch is virtually rainproof, and the twigs to which it is attached are so tough that it often hangs there in quite good condition for several years.

Wonderfully protected, too, is the five- to ten-foot burrow at the end of which a pair of belted king-fishers raise their half-dozen or more youngsters. Usually the old birds dig it near the top of a steep sand or gravel bank so it will be out of reach of robbers yet close enough to the roots of the coarse grass or shrubbery growing above it to avoid the risk of a cave-in.

Also, it slopes slightly upward from the entrance, so if any water seeps in, it will promptly run out. Finally, if some thug does manage to sneak in he is usually met by the fearless and highly formidable beak of whichever parent is on duty—a most painful experience, as you will remember if you ever thrust your arm into an occupied kingfisher tunnel when one of the old birds was at home.

Many birds take out their burglar insurance policies in the form of extremely dense bushes or other plant growth where the nest will be completely hidden as well as difficult to reach. Catbirds and song sparrows are familiar members of this group. Both frequently nest in barberry shrubs and climbing roses, where the protection of numerous tough twigs is supplemented by countless needle-sharp thorns.

Those pear-shaped nest cavities which woodpeckers chop in dead tree trunks or limbs also furnish splendid protection against storms and all manner of winged and four-footed enemies larger than their owners, excepting squirrels. These inquisitive beggars, particularly the red ones, sometimes enlarge the opening with their teeth so that they can squeeze through and feast on the eggs or helpless young—unless, of course, the parent woodpeckers beat them off.

Most interesting of all, perhaps, is the leaf-covered nest which the ovenbird builds directly on the ground. Even when you are only a yard away you cannot see it, so perfectly does it resemble its surroundings. Its roof is rounded, too, so as to shed rain, and the entrance is on the side. Long ago someone said that it looked like an old Dutch oven, and that was the origin of the bird's common name.

Kingfishers nest in high bank burrows for safety

The red-tailed and other hawks have incredibly keen eyes

Eagle Eyes

ALL BIRDS HAVE THEM,

WHETHER THEY ARE

LARGE OR SMALL

IF HUMAN EYES were one-tenth as good as a bird's, nobody would need to wear glasses and the manufacturers of telescopes and binoculars would have to switch to making neckties, chewing gum or some other popular commodity. Save for the marvelous compound eyes of insects, those of a bird are probably the world's most perfect optical instruments.

Have you ever watched a flock of pigeons sunning themselves on a barn roof? Then perhaps you have seen them suddenly tilt their heads to stare straight into the sky where, apparently, there was nothing more dangerous than limitless blue space. Yet if you had followed the direction of their gaze through a strong glass you might have spied a hawk, far beyond the limit of your unaided vision.

A bird's eye delineates far more sharply than ours. In part this is due to the relatively great size of the eye itself, and of that portion of the brain which, by way of the connecting nerves, records whatever impressions enter through the lens. Besides, the entire optic system is much more sensitive than ours and adjusts itself with great rapidity to changes of light, distance and other conditions which, to us, would mean an indistinct image or maybe none at all.

It is faculties such as these which enable your pigeon flock to detect the presence of a hawk that, to you, is completely out of sight. Similarly, the vulture soaring so high in air that it is hardly more than a speck to our eyes, sees a dead rabbit lying in the grass and glides down to the feast, a maneuver which other vultures miles away notice and quickly follow in the hope of arriving in time to share the meal.

So, too, a little sparrow hawk flying a hundred feet above a hayfield catches the slight movement of a mouse or grasshopper in the jungle of stems and blades and drops accurately for the kill. And the phoebe, perched on a sunlit branch across the stream, sights a tiny insect flying in the gloom under a bridge's arch and darts into the shadows to catch it deftly.

The marvels of bird vision are by no means limited to powers of sharp delineation such as these. Quite as remarkable is the ability of the eye to adjust its focus instantly to offset changes of distance, light and movement that to us would be completely baffling. This makes it possible for the hummingbird to dart through a maze of branches at terrific speed without touching one of them, and yet instantaneously select a certain twig and come to rest upon it as lightly as a feather. And more impressive even than this is the duck hawk, plunging on its quarry at 200 miles an hour and seeing the fleeing victim clearly right up to the moment of fatal impact. Only the best of eyes can do that, and the best is necessary in every bird's way of life.

New Times, New Customs

MOST BIRDS ARE DYED-IN-
THE-WOOL REACTIONARIES,
BUT A FEW—

FOR MANY THOUSANDS of years birds have
retained the habits handed down to them by their
ancestors, each species according to its own particular pattern. The majority never deviate, carrying
their faithfulness even to the point of deserting an
area if its character changes enough to interfere with
their ancient ways. Yet there are a few kinds that
have taken altered conditions in their stride and availed
themselves of facilities which only our human civiliza-
tion has laid before them.

The chimney swift is a striking example of this
ability to change with the times. Long before the first
man-made chimney was dreamed of our swifts roosted
and built their nests in hollow trees, as some still do
in very remote regions. But when chimneys appeared
on the scene the birds seemed to recognize their new
opportunity, and today that is the customary place to
find their strange, glued homes of twigs.

Tree swallows, too, formerly raised their families
only in tree cavities, taking what they could find where
they found it. But nowadays they readily accept indi-

vidual bird-boxes set up for them in the open-country situations which all swallows prefer because of their aerial method of hunting for their insect food. The closely allied purple martin, a confirmed colony-nester, has shifted with equal readiness from tree and cliff cavities to man-made homes, and today you may find a dozen or more pairs occupying a single tenement-type home season after season.

Robins, of course, have adapted themselves perfectly to the changes brought to their ancestral domain by the white man, and now nest on porch ledges, beam tops and other sheltered supports, as well as on their old-time tree limbs and crotches. You find an even more striking example of adaptability in the nighthawk, that fantastic looking character often referred to as "bull-bat" as it gyrates in the upper air feeding on high-flying insects. Always accustomed to laying its eggs on flat rocks or bare ground out in the country, the modern nighthawk makes itself quite at home in the heart of our largest cities where flat roofs, often surfaced with gravel, provide de luxe nesting sites despite the humming human life in the streets below.

And while we are on the subject of city environment, here is the most surprising case of all: the famous peregrine or duck hawk. From the ancient days of falconry this bold, incredibly swift freebooter has been noted for its fierce spirit and the wild, inaccessible cliffs on whose ledges it normally nests. Yet now, in New York, Philadelphia and other large cities the peregrine occasionally lays its several brown-blotched eggs in a cornice niche of a tall building hundreds of feet above street or avenue and right in the haunts of those pigeons which are among its favorite foods.

Before houses came, chimney swifts nested in hollow trees

A single kingbird is more than a match for the biggest crow

Chips on Their Shoulders

CERTAIN BIRDS ACT LIKE BULLIES BECAUSE THEY'RE BUILT THAT WAY

NEARLY ALL of our wild birds prefer peace to war and seldom become seriously aggressive except in the defense of home and family. In view of this general situation, and also because the exceptions to it are so difficult to explain, the chip-on-the-shoulder nature of a few species is particularly intriguing.

One of the most peppery of these battlers is also the tiniest—our tenth-ounce ruby-throated humming-bird. This minute imp is forever attacking crows, hawks and other relatively monstrous birds, darting around them like a furious hornet and jabbing so effectively with its needle bill that the lumbering victim is soon routed. The reason for such ferocity is obscure; certainly the hummer need not fear destruction of its eggs or young, for both are too small to be of much interest to such a big nest robber. If bird psychology were like ours, a good guess might be that the feathered atom has a terrible inferiority complex and is trying to build up its ego.

Similar hostility toward species far larger than

themselves characterizes the kingbirds, members of the "tyrant" branch of the flycatcher tribe. Though normally peaceful toward most of the bird community, all kingbird species react violently to every big fellow —even an eagle—that comes within sight of their chosen territories. The gray kingbird, a southern representative of the group, goes so far as to attack animals and even people. Home defense is doubtless a primary factor in such behavior, but the great distances to which kingbirds often chase intruders indicate that family safety may not be the whole story.

Another chip-on-the-shoulder bird is the scissor-tailed flycatcher of our southwestern states, a showy, streamer-tailed fellow that adds spectacular flying gymnastics to the vigor of its attack. Here again there is general agreement on the part that family protection plays in the pursuit, but no one really familiar with scissor-tails could deny their habitual attitude of cocky aggressiveness and almost swaggering self-confidence.

To conclude these partial notes on birds with more than a normal share of scrappiness, let's take a quick look at a highly lauded American, the mockingbird. This Southerner, possessed of an astoundingly broad and incessant vocal repertoire, figuratively carries a chip on each shoulder all the time. A mocker will battle just about anything that nears its nesting place. Crows, hawks and cats are violently pursued and human beings threatened. Even before its own nesting season begins, a mocker will fight home-seeking purple martins and bluebirds whose nesting boxes happen to have become its favorite perching spots while they were vacant. There seems little doubt that mockingbirds just like a row!

Time to Change Clothes

EVEN FEATHER SUITS

WEAR OUT,

AND THAT'S NOT ALL

TO US HUMANS who know that a suit of clothes or a dress cannot last forever, the birds' habit of periodically discarding their old feathers and growing new ones seems natural enough. The surprising things about it are the complexity of the procedure and the profound bearing it has on the lives of the creatures involved.

Most of our smaller land birds are stark naked when hatched, except for some thin down on the upper half of their bodies. This is quickly followed by the appearance of pinfeathers which expand into the nestling or first real plumage in one or two weeks. These feathers are the ones worn by the youngsters when they leave the nest, but soon all are discarded except most of those in the wings and tail, and are replaced by fresh ones which may or may not resemble those of the parents. This new set constitutes the first winter suit, and is worn until spring brings another molt, variable in completeness and succeeded by the first breeding plumage. In most species the colors and markings are now identical with those of the old birds.

After the nesting season the yearlings embark on their fully adult, lifetime schedule: a complete but gradual summer molt; replacement by the winter plumage; and another variable spring change that, among the males of many species, brings those brighter colors that mark the approach of the annual marriage season. At all times enough full-size wing and tail feathers are in operation to maintain the power of flight.

So much for the general clothes-changing system followed by the majority of land birds as well as other large groups. Now for a few of its curious variations found in certain species.

The young of gulls, terns, shore-birds and fowllike kinds such as bob-whites, grouse and pheasants are densely down-covered when they hatch and are prepared to leave the nest and run about strongly within a few hours. Also, the last group adds enough wing-feather growth to enable them to fly while still wearing their natal down, an important asset when you consider the number of ground predators to which their way of life exposes them.

Most swimming birds lose all their old wingfeathers during the summer molt and for a time are unable to fly. For this period of comparative helplessness, male ducks go into an additional "eclipse" molt in which the head, neck, breast and some shoulder feathers are replaced by others similar to the unobtrusive colors of the females. The normal bright male pattern is resumed only when the new wing quills have developed sufficiently for flying. And finally, male goldfinches and scarlet tanagers change only their body feathers in preparation for the breeding season, while bobolinks do a complete job of it.

A male bobolink in gay spring suit and sober autumn one

*Brown thrashers are grand singers with a gift
for mimicry*

Mimics and Ventriloquists

SOME ARE SO CLEVER
THAT THEY REALLY
KEEP YOU GUESSING

MIMICRY, WITH US, is largely an entertainment stunt, amusing at parties and sometimes on the stage. There is no mystery about why we do it, or why a realistic imitation tickles our fancy. But so far as I am aware no one has offered any real explanation why certain birds make a habit of giving excellent vocal imitations of other species and even of man-made sounds.

Perhaps the best known of these feathered mimics is the mockingbird, whose voluble song is a medley of just about all the sounds that you can imagine coming from a bird's throat. Doglike barks, the crowing of roosters and cackling of hens, the coo of a dove, the postman's whistle, squeaks of a rusty hinge, even the notes of a piano played on a summer evening—these are a few of the variations that a male mocker tosses at random into his prolonged outpourings. To be sure, some authorities hesitate to brand them as deliberate imitations, and incline to the theory that they are merely inherent parts of the repertoire with which mockingbirds are naturally endowed and which happen to resemble sounds originating in other sources. But the general consensus is that most of them are simon-pure imitations.

The catbird is somewhat less gifted in the art of sounding like something else, but still rates as our second-best bird mimic. Its song is less strident and sustained than a mocker's, and on occasion far more truly musical. But if you listen to it carefully day after day you will detect interpolations of various other distinctive bird voices, such as those of the crested flycatcher, kingfisher, Baltimore oriole, cardinal and towhee. So, too, with our third acknowledged mimic bird, the brown thrasher, a gifted singer in its own right and as personable a feathered neighbor as you will find anywhere. Even the blue jay often impersonates the "scream" of a red-shouldered hawk with striking fidelity—its only obvious imitation, so far as I have heard.

Ventriloquism by birds is far less frequent than mimicry. Among our everyday American species it is limited to hardly more than three: the rose-breasted grosbeak, scarlet tanager and Carolina wren. Even these are by no means lavish with their strange gift; as a rule their voices come to your ears as straight as arrows. But on occasion all three will "throw" their notes so successfully that you feel sure they are uttered from a point yards away from their owner's actual location. When, as often happens, the speaker is well hidden among green summer leaves, the trick becomes so baffling that you begin to wonder whether it's your eyes or ears that are at fault. And by the time you think you have settled that question, the singer has generally flown elsewhere.

[98]

Some Carry Their Babies

THOUGH HAVING NEITHER
HANDS NOR POCKETS, THEY
MANAGE VERY WELL

IT IS PERFECTLY normal for people, cats and monkeys to carry their small offspring to other places when danger threatens or some necessity requires, but birds—well, you wouldn't expect such things from them. Yet the fact remains that a few kinds do exactly this.

Granted that a parent bird should decide to carry its young away, grasping it firmly yet gently in those flexible motherly feet would seem to be the obvious method. However, this appears to be rarely, if ever, done. Probably whip-poor-wills and woodcock come the closest to it when they move their infants one at a time by clasping them between their legs before taking wing. Specific data on the frequency of such transportation is scanty, but the chances are that the old birds resort to it only in an extremity, for it seems precarious at best.

The wood duck conducts its rescue operations along different lines. This handsome and completely engaging little webfoot customarily nests in large tree cavities from a yard to forty feet or so from the ground, and lays up to a dozen or fifteen eggs in one clutch. A day or so after they hatch the ducklings begin to clamber out of the hole, making effective use of their sharp little claws and the hook with which each bill tip is equipped at this stage. If the trunk is slanting they may climb down it to join their mother on the ground or water below, or they may flutter and tumble part of the way. Not infrequently the old bird avoids all this by giving them a ride down in her bill or, as some competent observers report, riding on her back two or three at a time. Once fully reunited the whole family abandons the nest for good and thereafter leads a regular duck life.

Closely similar habits of tree nesting and rather rough-and-ready journeying to the ground or water by the youngsters characterize the hooded merganser, another small fresh-water duck which, in its way, is almost as pretty as the wood duck. As with the preceding species, it is the female that takes full charge of the transportation problem as well as the subsequent general care of the brood.

I know of no prettier scene in bird life than a mother hooded and her wee brood gliding like toy boats along the shore of a wilderness lake, each mirrored perfectly in the dark, glassy water. Now and then a youngster dives in pursuit of a water beetle, popping up again like a cork a few feet away. And often a duckling or two, perhaps tired from swimming, will scramble to the mother's back and ride along with an air of satisfaction and utter confidence that is worth going a long way to see.

*Baby hooded mergansers love to ride on their
mother's back*

A drum roll with his wings is the ruffed grouse's song

Queer Ways to Sing

WHEN IT COMES TO MUSIC,
BIRDS HAVE UNIQUE CUSTOMS

ORDINARILY the singing of a bird is a mere matter of expanding the lungs, opening the mouth and uttering more or less musical notes much as we humans do. But the songs of some kinds sound as if they could not possibly be made by the vocal cords, while others do not involve the use of voice or even lungs.

Wood pewees definitely belong in the first of these categories, for they sing *Pee-wee, pe-ah-wee* with the exact tonal quality of a whistle, though if you see one in action he'll have his bill wide open as if to prove that it's really done with the throat. The tufted titmouse, too, sings precisely as if he were whistling, and so do several of the wren family. For still another perfectly whistlelike song you have only to listen to a male eastern meadowlark on a spring day.

A male bittern, that heronlike oddity often called stake-driver, marsh hen and dunk-a-doo, has a weird song the end of which sounds like somebody hitting the end of a stake with a heavy mallet. This is preceded by gulping intakes of air that inflate a special sac in the bird's neck. Suddenly this air is expelled with a hollow, booming sound, followed by a sharp *ka*—the mallet stroke.

Nighthawks also follow the *boom* theme, though they play it entirely with their wings as they pull suddenly out of a power dive from high in air almost to the ground. And a male ruffed grouse, when he feels like singing in the spring—and sometimes in the fall as well—also scorns to use his voice in the performance. Instead, he mounts an old log or maybe a boulder or stump deep in the woods, draws himself up to his full height and strikes downward with his wings so powerfully that the successive blows, at first well spaced and then rapidly accelerating, produce the muffled drum roll for which he is famous. It used to be thought that these far-carrying thuds resulted from the wings striking the bird's sides, but it is now believed that they come entirely from the sudden impact of feathers against air.

Equally strange are the drumming songs sounded by the males of several woodpecker species when mating time urges them to express themselves. These are a characteristic early spring sound out in the country, audible sometimes for a quarter-mile or more and repeated many times by the same bird. If you approach cautiously you may catch a glimpse of him clinging to a dead limb high in a tree, beating out his amazing tattoo with his bill. He seems to have a critical ear for music, too, for often he tries several spots on different limbs before finding one that gives the particular tone he wants. Once the selection is made he will stay with it through the whole drumming season unless some unusual occurrence intervenes.

Long Journey

EVERY AUTUMN the majority of our North American birds fly southward, some of them three or four hundred miles and others ten times that distance. Each spring they return over more or less the same routes to build their nests and raise their young. These, in a nutshell, are the movements that we call migration.

It is an incredible picture, this semi-annual trek by hundreds of species and billions of individuals, from three-inch hummingbirds weighing less than a half-ounce to cranes five feet long and geese and swans that may tip the scales at a dozen pounds or more. It originated, most authorities believe, when the onset of the Ice Age began to change the temperate climate of polar regions to an increasingly frigid one that caused many birds to retreat before it. Finally came the glaciers, creeping implacably southward and forcing more and more birds into our present tropical areas and pinning them there for eons.

At last the ice cap commenced its own retreat, and as the released regions began to grow warmer the exiled birds returned toward their old haunts. The climate of the Northern Hemisphere, as we know it, was in the making: warmer as the earth's orbit brings the sun northward in the spring, chilling again as the process is reversed. And the birds followed the sun, for only in that way could they be assured of the temperatures and food supplies essential to their existence through the seasons.

Over these millions of years our present bird and animal life evolved, passing through changes too vast and varied to be fully grasped by any human mind. Yet in a sense, if we accept this theory of migration's origin, the basis of what is now a deeply rooted bird instinct is not too obscure. Many of its details, however, are still cloaked in mystery.

For one thing, science is divided on how generation after generation of migratory birds finds its way so unerringly, often under cover of darkness, over such huge land and water areas. Birds carry no compass devices, so far as we know, and certainly a good memory for landmarks cannot be the full answer for the simple reason that the multitudes of young birds making the southward journey each fall have never before flown the route. Presumably there is some sort of involuntary nerve or brain reaction that holds the travellers on their course, possibly a guiding power of which we have no knowledge. It is easy to say simply that birds have "a good sense of direction" or "a homing instinct," just as some people do. But what kind of sense is it, and how and in what part of the brain or nerve system does it function? Perhaps some day we shall find the answer, but that time has not yet come.

Canada geese, spectacular symbols of the migration flight

Early spring spurs the purple grackles to sing in chorus

Gentlemen First

A MIGRATION HABIT THAT
SERVES A PARTICULAR
PURPOSE

SO FAR AS our smaller spring migrants are concerned, the males often arrive from the South ten days or two weeks earlier than the females. Red-winged blackbirds are familiar examples of this advance-guard operation, and robins are another. The males of both these species seem to delight in telling the world that they've come back, too, for one of the first things they do is to sing on every possible occasion. With blackbirds, especially, this vocalizing often takes the form of regular group performances, as though the gang was having its last good time together before settling down to family duties.

The reasons underlying this preseason movement of the males are not too clear, but they may well concern the selection of suitable nesting territories before the time comes to mate and raise families. As outlined in the chapter on the motives for bird songs, each pair will choose and defend its own home grounds, and a preliminary survey of the possibilities sounds like good common sense.

Starlings walk and sparrows hop—both for good reasons

Hoppers and Walkers

IT'S MAINLY A QUESTION
OF WHERE YOU SPEND
YOUR LIFE

HAVE YOU EVER wondered why some kinds of
birds that you see on the ground move about
by hopping with both feet together, while others
walk or run with alternate steps the way people do?
Or why the same bird—a sparrow, for example—
sometimes hops one minute and runs the next? Well,
the explanation is simpler than you might expect.

For the most part, the hopping style is followed by
birds that live chiefly in trees where both feet must
be used simultaneously in grasping twigs and other
tricky footholds. Out-and-out ground dwellers, on the
other hand, such as bob-whites and sandpipers, are so
accustomed to level, substantial footing that they walk
or trot in the ordinary way. So do other non-perching
birds, like ducks, geese and gulls.

Then there are those that both walk and hop. They
are the ones that divide their time more or less equally
between the ground and trees, shrubs, weed stalks and
other airy growths, and govern their steps according to
where they are.

Empty egg shells must be removed, as wrens and others know

Sanitation Department

CLEANLINESS IS NEXT TO GODLINESS, EVEN AMONG BIRDS

IF YOU HAVE watched a pair of our common songbirds—wrens, catbirds or bluebirds, perhaps—bringing nourishment to their nestlings you may have been mystified by seeing the old bird leave the nest at intervals with a small white object in its bill. Clearly, it seemed to be the wrong direction for any parent to be carrying food.

Actually, you were witnessing the sanitation department at work, for those small burdens were a young bird's excrement automatically encased in thin membrane for easy disposal at a safe distance. This custom is followed by all the "perching" birds, which constitute a major proportion of our everyday feathered population. Except for it, the nest would quickly become so fouled that the health of its inmates would suffer.

Another clean-up chore of the parents is to dispose of the egg shells as soon as the young have hatched. It is interesting to note that they are dropped some distance away, perhaps to avoid disclosing the nest's location.

*Killdeers and other young birds heed the warning
to "freeze"*

Obedience Begins at Home

AND LITTLE BIRDS LEARN
IT VERY FAST—OR ELSE

THE STAGE AT WHICH the fear instinct in young birds develops enough to result in some kind of evasive action varies with the species, but in general it becomes really evident shortly before they leave the nest. At this age the warning notes of the parents are believed to be a major influence in causing the youngsters to remain still as death, or "freeze," in the face of any real disturbance that may mean danger.

Among the most striking examples of obedience to parental orders is the behavior of those species which leave the nest soon after hatching, like the ducks, grouse and terns. Even when only a day or two out of the shell these active infants run or swim about freely, yet they will respond instantly to the old bird's warning call—the brood of ducklings scattering far and wide over the water, while grouse and tern children squat motionless on the ground, depending on their protective coloring to save them, until the "all clear" signal tells them it is all right to go on about their business.

[115]

*For a bird of prey, the barred owl looks
surprisingly gentle*

Bird Temperament

OFTEN IT IS STARTINGLY
LIKE THAT OF SOME HUMANS

THE CHARACTERS of birds differ almost as much as do those of people, with this important qualification: their variations apply to whole species, not merely to individuals. It is worth noting, too, that these temperamental differences appear to be counterparts of many that are found in the human race—calmness, quick temper, gentleness, self-assertion, greed, and so on.

You can no more miss the aggressiveness of English sparrows and starlings than you could overlook the retiring ways of mourning doves and most of the wood warblers. The caution and at the same time the curiosity of the wrens are equally outstanding and contrast sharply with the placid trustfulness of a chipping sparrow. Robins, on the other hand, can be complete scatter-brains when deciding where to raise their families, and may even change their minds after the nest is fully built. And for sheer calculated boldness it would be hard to surpass the peregrine falcon that kills a pigeon almost at the rooftops of a great city and devours it on a convenient building ledge.

A peregrine falcon can power-dive at 200 miles an hour

Speed Demons

FACTS AND FIGURES ON
A SUBJECT TOO LITTLE
UNDERSTOOD

THE MAXIMUM flying speed of a bird is not easy to determine, for it depends not only on the species you have in mind, but also on variables such as favorable or adverse winds, the degree of urgency that the flier feels, the distance being flown, and so on. However, here are some estimates based on reliable data that throw interesting light on the matter.

Many species, including ducks, geese, shorebirds, starlings and mourning doves, can hit at least a mile-a-minute clip when frightened. Our ruby-throated hummingbird does fully as well, despite its minute size; its breast flying muscles, as you know, are relatively enormous.

The world's speed championship is thought to lie between the peregrine falcon or duck hawk and one or another of the swift tribe, of which the chimney swift is our common American representative. Peregrines normally cruise at 40 to 60 miles an hour, and more than triple this speed in their spectacular power dives. Possibly, swifts are even faster!

Great blue herons are skilled stalkers and rarely miss

The Spear Hunters

MASTERS OF THE CAREFUL

STALK AND SUDDEN,

DEADLY THRUST

THE MARGINS and shallow bays of rivers, ponds and lakes are the places to watch the spear hunters at their work. There, especially in early morning and toward evening from mid-spring to autumn, you can see them standing like sentinels or stalking through the quiet water with the deliberate stealth of athletes shown on the movie screen with a slow-motion projector.

Long of leg and neck, adept in the arts of approaching a wary quarry and delivering a final stroke that drives a spear-shaped bill unerringly to its mark, these huntsmen of the heron tribe are at once grotesque and supremely successful in their task. They will stand as motionless as statues for many minutes, waiting for an unwary fish, eel or frog to swim within striking distance. At other times they wade for many yards without stirring a ripple, in search of more productive fishing grounds. Utter patience is one of their big stocks in trade, and they rarely fail to turn it to good account in the form of a square meal of fresh-killed food.